GW00865064

MY FIRST
BIBLE ACTIVITY BOOK
EASTER
DAYS

LEENA LANE AND ANNA TODD

Jesus rides on a donkey

Jesus and his friends came near to Jerusalem.

'Fetch a donkey from the village over there,' said Jesus, pointing to some houses nearby. 'If anyone asks you what you are doing, tell them that the Lord needs it.'

Jesus' friends fetched the donkey.

Jesus sat on the donkey's back and rode along the road into the busy city of Jerusalem.

Many people watched Jesus coming and threw their cloaks on the road in front of the donkey. Other people cut palm branches off the trees and spread them on the road. Everybody waved and cheered.

'The King is coming!' they shouted. 'Hosanna! Praise God!'

1 2 3 4 5

Can you see four more children in the crowd?
Draw an arrow and put a circle round each one.

J A F C L O A K P P U T
B A P A L K L G S A K H
F J E S U S S P L L I E
J S S D O N K E Y M N R
D E J T S F Y M C K G A

Can you find the words JESUS, DONKEY, PALM, KING and CLOAK?
Trace over the letters in another colour so they stand out.

Join these dots to see the animal Jesus rode into Jerusalem.

Jesus is angry

When Jesus and his friends arrived in Jerusalem, Jesus went to the temple. But when he got there Jesus was angry. This was supposed to be God's house, but it was full of people buying and selling things. Jesus turned over all the tables of the moneychangers and the stools where the pigeon-sellers were sitting.

'God wants this to be a house of prayer, not a den of thieves!' said Jesus.

Can you join up each broken jar? Draw a line from each jar top to the matching bottom.

Can you find two coins which look the same? Draw a line to join them up.

Look at these pictures.
Can you find these things in the big picture? Draw a circle round them if you can.

Can you find where these five details belong in the big picture?

Write the number of each shape in the correct space in the big picture.

1
2
3
4
5

The story of the ten girls

Jesus told his friends a story to show them how
to be ready for God's kingdom:

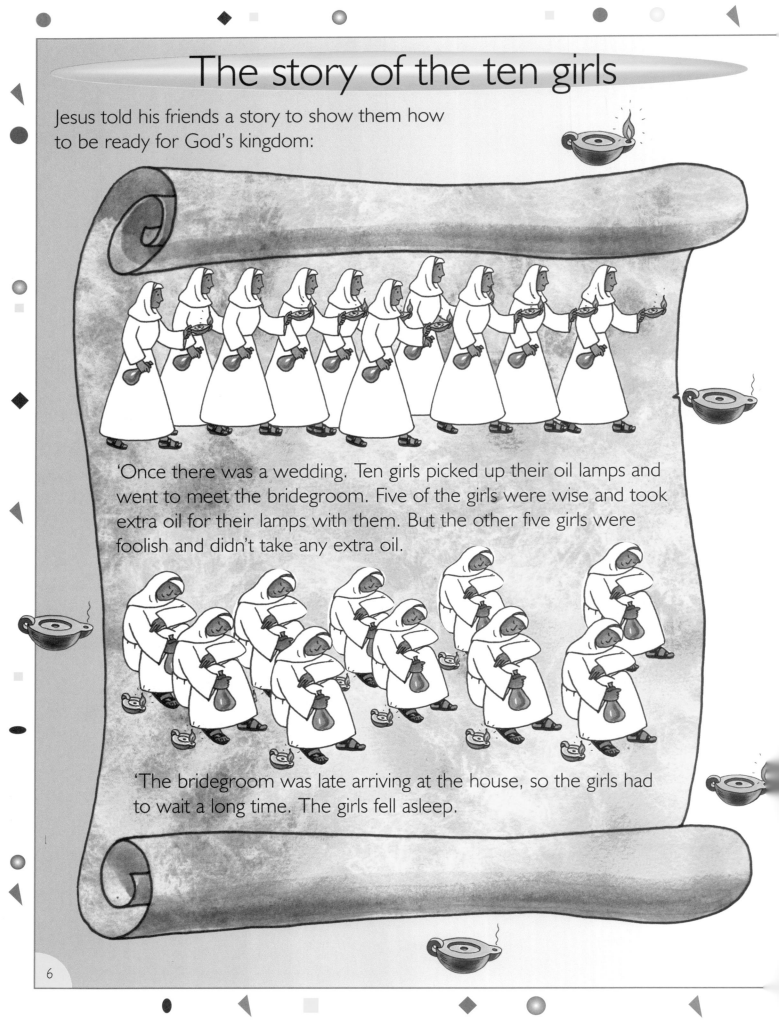

'Once there was a wedding. Ten girls picked up their oil lamps and
went to meet the bridegroom. Five of the girls were wise and took
extra oil for their lamps with them. But the other five girls were
foolish and didn't take any extra oil.

'The bridegroom was late arriving at the house, so the girls had
to wait a long time. The girls fell asleep.

Put a circle round the full oil lamps and draw a square round the empty ones.

How many lamps are there altogether? Write the number in the box.

'Suddenly there was a shout: "The bridegroom is coming!" All the girls woke up.

'By now the oil in their lamps had run out. The five wise girls put their extra oil in their lamps and the lamps burned brightly. But the five foolish girls had to go off and buy some more oil.

'While they were away, the bridegroom arrived. They missed him because they were not ready.'

Can you finish colouring in the people in the story?

Jesus washes his friends' feet

Can you find the mistake in this picture? Draw a circle round it.

Jesus knew that he would soon have to leave his friends and go to be with God. He met with his friends for a special meal.

Before they sat down to eat, Jesus tied a towel round his waist. He poured some water into a bowl. Then he started to wash his friends' hot, dusty feet.

'What are you doing?' asked Peter. 'I won't let you wash my feet! You are my master, not my servant!'

'Let me wash your feet,' said Jesus.

At last Peter agreed.

Then Jesus said, 'I have washed your feet. Now you should wash one another's feet. Look after each other as I am caring for you.'

Follow the footprints to see whose feet were dirty, whose feet were clean and who was wearing shoes.
Draw the right footprints in each box.

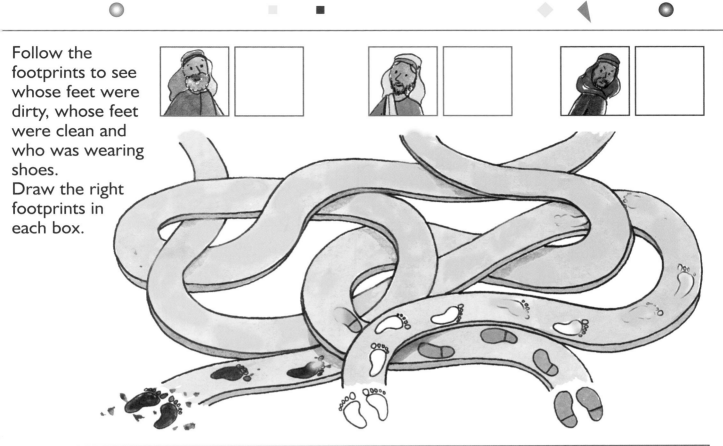

These feet appear on another page in this book.
Who do they belong to and which page are they on?

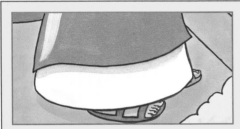

Name	Page

Can you help these three people find their own shoes?

For each pair of feet draw a line connected to the right size shoes.

Write a 'b' in the box under the biggest feet.

Write an 's' under the smallest feet.

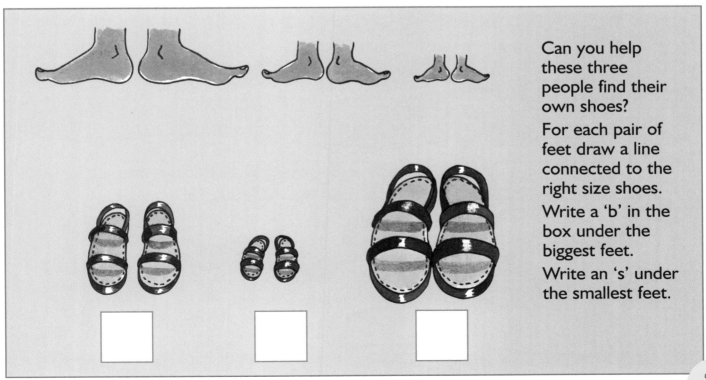

9

The Last Supper

Jesus sat down with his friends to eat the Passover supper. It was a special meal when people remembered the time when God rescued Moses and the Israelites in Egypt.

Jesus told his friends that he would soon be going away from them.

Jesus picked up the cup of wine, said thank you to God, then passed it around amongst his friends.

'Take this and drink it,' he said. 'This is my blood.'

Look carefully at these things connected with the Last Supper Jesus ate. Put your hand over the picture and see how many you can remember.

Then Jesus took some bread, said thank you to God, broke it and passed it around amongst his friends, saying:

'Take this and eat it. This is my body. Do this to remember me when I am gone.'

Jesus' friends didn't understand what he meant. Where was Jesus going?

Then Judas quietly left the room to betray Jesus to his enemies.

Finish colouring in the picture of the Last Supper.

Count how many friends Jesus has and put the number in the box. Draw a circle around Judas.

Write the number of plates you can see on the table.

How many loaves of bread are there on the table?

There are not enough oranges for everyone on the table. How many of the people at the table will not be able to have one?

Jesus prays in the garden

After the meal, Jesus left the house and went to the Mount of Olives with his friends. He wanted to pray to God in the Garden of Gethsemane. He told his friends to pray too.

Jesus prayed, 'Father God, please help me.'

Jesus was very worried about what was going to happen to him, but he knew that he wanted to do whatever pleased God.

Jesus went back to his friends. They had fallen asleep!

'Don't go to sleep!' said Jesus. 'Get up and pray with me!'

Then Judas, who had been one of Jesus' twelve friends, came up to him, leading a group of soldiers. Judas showed the soldiers who Jesus was, and they took Jesus away.

Jesus' friends were frightened.
They ran away.

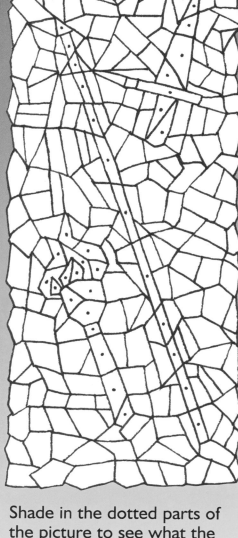

Shade in the dotted parts of the picture to see what the soldiers brought with them.

Count how many friends are running away and write the number here.

Which of these five things would you run away from?
Draw a circle round them.

Some people are afraid of spiders.

Can you find seven more spiders hiding on these pages?

Peter lets Jesus down

Peter really loved Jesus. He thought he was one of Jesus' best friends. But Jesus told him that soon Peter would pretend he didn't know Jesus at all. Peter said that he would never do that—he would always be Jesus' friend.

'No, Peter,' said Jesus. 'Before the cock crows tonight, you will say three times that you don't know me.'

Peter was very upset when the soldiers took Jesus away. He followed them and waited outside the house.

A servant girl was sitting nearby and saw Peter warming himself at the fire.

'This is one of Jesus' friends!' she said.

Peter said three times that he didn't know Jesus.
In the big picture there are seven things that are drawn in groups of three. Draw a line around each group.

Colour in this picture of the crowing cockerel.

Use the colouring guide below to help you.

'No, I don't know who Jesus is,' said Peter.
They asked him three times if he knew Jesus. Each time, Peter said no.
Suddenly a cockerel crowed and Peter remembered Jesus' words. Peter felt terrible. He had let down his best friend.

Jesus was brought before the Roman governor who was called Pontius Pilate.

'What has this man done wrong?' asked Pilate.

'He is causing trouble all over the country,' said the chief priests. 'He says he is a king.'

'Are you the king of the Jews?' asked Pilate.

'Yes,' said Jesus.

'What shall I do with Jesus?' Pilate asked the crowd.

'Put him on a cross to die!' they shouted.

Pilate did not think Jesus had done anything wrong, but he was afraid that a riot might start.

So Pilate handed Jesus over to the soldiers to be killed. The soldiers put a purple robe on him and a crown of thorns on his head.

They mocked him and jeered, then led him away.

Three of these soldiers were on duty at the trial.
Draw a circle round the one who was not there.

Can you find three things that should not be in the big picture?

The Romans didn't use numbers like we do. They used letters like this:

I = 1
V = 5
X = 10

How many Roman soldiers are there in the big picture? Write your answer in Roman letters.

How many people are there behind the soldiers? Write your answer in Roman letters.

Write the answer to this sum:

V + V =

What is this figure in numbers?

XVI

Write the name of this object here.

_____

Write the name of the man it was made for.

_____

Jesus dies on a cross

On Friday, Jesus was taken to a place on a hill called Golgotha. There he was put on a cross between two robbers. Jesus had done nothing wrong.

Jesus' friend John was looking after his mother, Mary. All Jesus' close friends were there. They were very upset. Why did Jesus have to die on a cross?

There were three crosses on the hill that terrible day. Can you mark three cross shapes in the box?

Jesus called out to God in a loud voice. Then darkness covered the whole land and Jesus died.

Jesus' body was taken down from the cross and placed in a special cave called a tomb. A large stone was rolled against the doorway. Everyone thought that they would never see Jesus again.

Draw a line to these people in the picture.
Mary, arm raised, comforted by John.
Eleven soldiers guarding the crosses.
Two robbers, crucified with Jesus.

Can you join all the dots using twelve lines to form a cross?

Where has Jesus gone?

Early on Sunday morning, Mary went to the tomb to take special spices to anoint Jesus' body.

But when she got there, she found that the large stone in front of the tomb had been rolled away and the tomb was empty. Jesus' body had

gone! All that was left were the strips of cloth in which his body had been wrapped.

Where had Jesus gone?

The garden is full of fruit trees and grapevines.

How many of the following can you find in the big picture?

Palm trees

Olive trees

Grape bunches

Fig trees

Can you find all the differences between these two pictures? Draw a line to point to each difference.

One has been done. There are nine more to find.

1 2 3 4 5 6 7 8 9 10

Angels

Mary and her friends were very surprised to find that Jesus' body had gone. Who could have rolled the big stone away? It was very heavy.

Suddenly, two men in bright shining clothes appeared.

'Why are you looking for Jesus here?' they asked the women. 'He is not dead. He is alive again!'

The women were amazed and ran off to tell all Jesus' friends what had happened.

Mary ran to tell her friends the good news.

Follow the paths to help her find the right road to the village.

The stone was very heavy.

Can you sort all the objects in order of weight? Write number 1 under the lightest object and number 7 under the heaviest.

Jesus is alive!

Jesus is
_____

Mary had been crying.
Who had taken her friend Jesus
away?

Mary heard a voice. She
turned round. A man was standing
there. Was it the gardener?

'Mary!' said the man.

Mary knew that voice.

It was Jesus!

Mary ran off to tell everyone the amazing
news. Jesus had died, but now he really had come
alive again!

Write down how many
of each of the
following things you
can find in the picture.

Jesus appears to his friends

Two of Jesus' friends were on their way to a village called Emmaus, near Jerusalem. They talked a lot about Jesus.

A little while later, another man came and walked alongside them. They didn't know who he was. He asked them lots of questions about Jesus. The two friends

Can you complete the roadsign?

E

told him how Jesus had been put on a cross, how he had been put in the tomb and how the women had found the tomb empty.

As they came near to Emmaus, the two friends asked the man to come and eat with them. The man sat down and picked up some bread. He broke it into smaller pieces and thanked God for it.

Suddenly they knew who this man was—it was Jesus! He was alive!

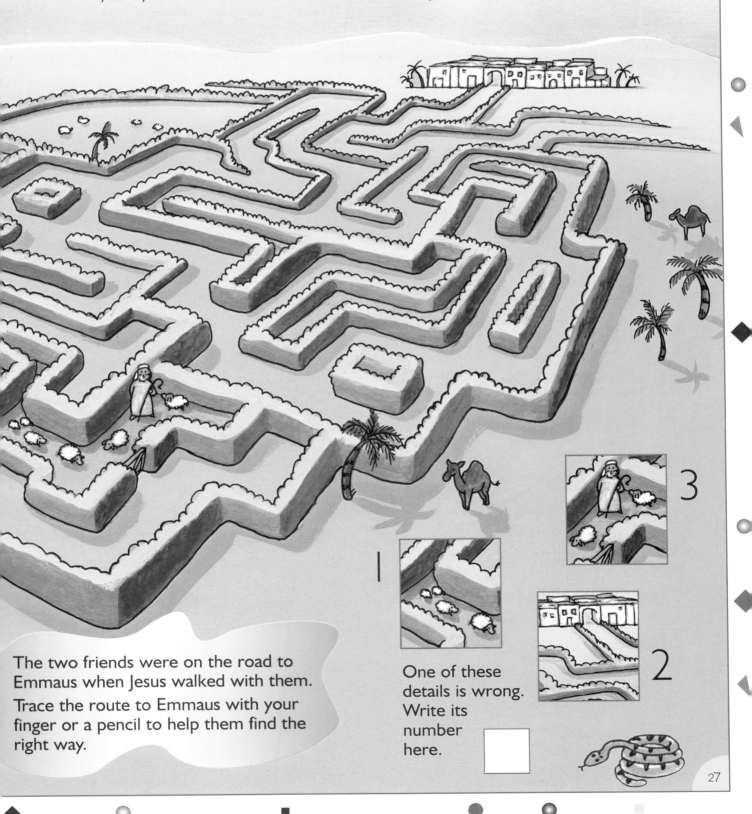

The two friends were on the road to Emmaus when Jesus walked with them.

Trace the route to Emmaus with your finger or a pencil to help them find the right way.

One of these details is wrong. Write its number here.

Thomas

One of Jesus' friends was called Thomas. When the others told him that Jesus was alive again, Thomas didn't believe it.

'He can't be,' said Thomas. 'It's impossible.'

'But we've seen Jesus!' said the other friends.

'Well,' said Thomas, 'I won't believe Jesus is alive unless I see his sore hands and feet from when he was on the cross.'

A week later, Jesus came to see all his friends.

Jesus said to Thomas, 'Look at my hands and feet, Thomas. Now do you believe it is me—your friend Jesus?'

Thomas knew at once that it was Jesus. 'You believe now that you have seen me,' said Jesus. 'There are some people who will be very happy by believing I am alive, even though they haven't seen me.'

Who was the first person to see Jesus alive again?

How many days did Thomas have to wait to see Jesus for himself?

Join the dots to see what Jesus showed Thomas.
You can colour in the picture.

Thomas could not believe that it was really Jesus.

Can you recognize which of these pictures is Jesus?
Tick the two pictures that are of Jesus and put a cross under the three pictures that are not Jesus.

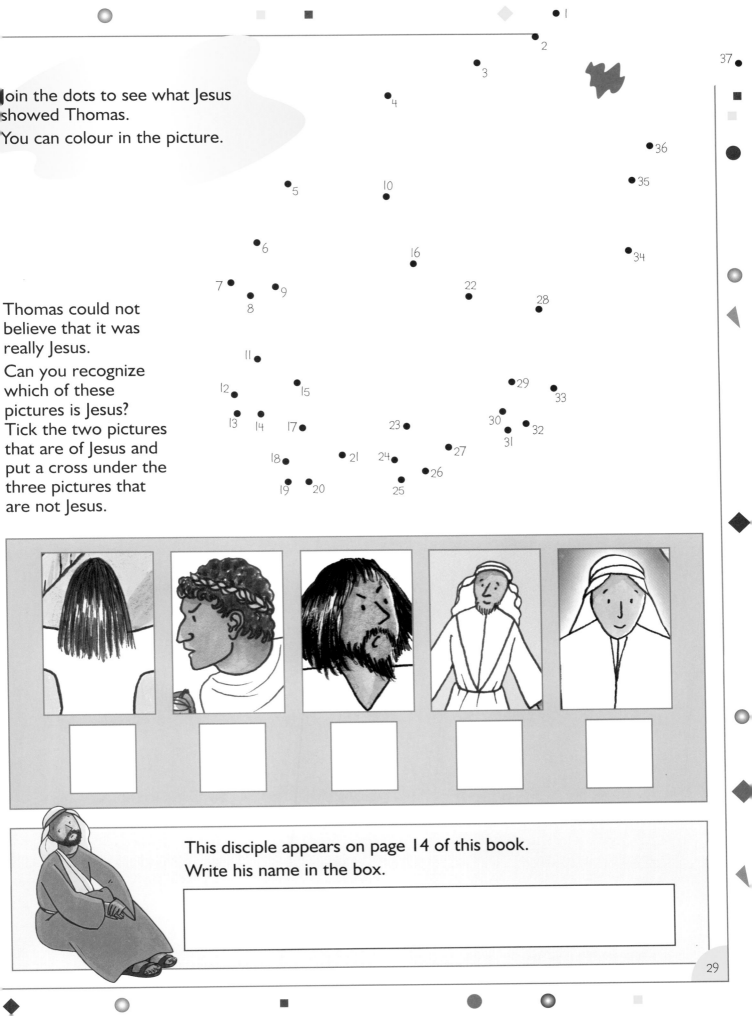

This disciple appears on page 14 of this book.
Write his name in the box.

Jesus cooks breakfast on the beach

Jesus appeared once more to his friends on the shores of a lake. Peter, Thomas and five other friends were fishing on the lake. They had tried to catch fish all night, but hadn't caught a thing.

A man called from the shore.

'Throw your net on the other side of the boat and you will catch lots of fish!' he said.

The friends did as he said and suddenly the net was filled with so many fish that they could hardly hold on to it!

Simon Peter knew at once who the man on the shore was. It was Jesus! Peter jumped into the water and ran to shore. Jesus was on the beach, cooking fish. They all ate together on the beach. It was so good to see Jesus again!

There are five different sorts of fish in the net.

Colour each of them to show they are different and write down the number of each type of fish in the boxes.

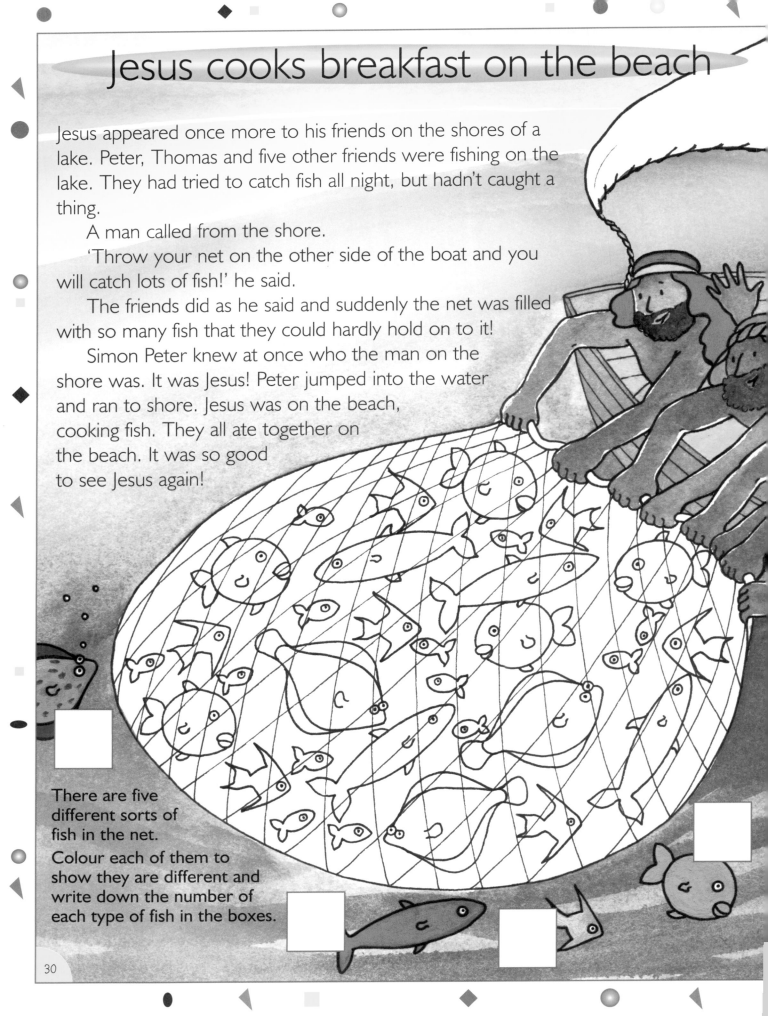

How many of
Jesus' friends
are fishing in
the boat?

Here are two
pictures of Jesus
cooking fish on
the beach.

Can you find
six differences
between them?
Draw a line from
the number to
each difference
on this picture.

1 2 3 4 5 6

Published by The Bible Reading Fellowship
15 The Chambers, Vineyard, Abingdon, Oxfordshire, OX14 3FE,
United Kingdom
ISBN 978-1-84101-560-6

First edition 2008
Reprinted 2009

Copyright © 2008 Anno Domini Publishing, Book House,
Orchard Mews, 18 High Street, Tring, Herts, HP23 5AH,
England
Text copyright © 2008 Anno Domini Publishing, Leena Lane
Text and illustrations copyright © 2008 Anna Todd

Editorial Director Annette Reynolds
Editor Nicola Bull
Art Director Gerald Rogers
Pre-production Krystyna Kowalska Hewitt
Production John Laister

British Library Cataloguing in Publication Data.
A catalogue record for this book is available from the British Library.

Printed and bound in Singapore.

Can you find all these
animals in the book?
Write the page number
in the red boxes.